Moms on Call

Basic Baby Essentials
Volume One: 0-6 Months

"A mom's best friend"

Developed by
Laura Hunter, LPN and
Jennifer Walker, RN, BSN

Instructional DVD
Included!!

Moms on Call – Basic Baby Essentials

Family cover photo by Jenny Fritzges

Baby cover photo by Jack Harrington

Cover design by Tim Walker

Formatting and book design by Rebecca Hayes

Editing by Tim Walker

Published in the United States by
Moms on Call, LLC
13 Crestview Drive
Dallas, GA 30157

In conjunction with
Cedar Hill Publishing
Snowflake, Arizona

ISBN 1-932373-98-5

Library of Congress Control Number:
2005900162

Moms-On-Call would first like to thank the Living God, who guided each step and gave purpose to our hearts. You are so spectacular and loving! May all blessing and honor and glory be to You.

There were so many families that have encouraged and uplifted us along the way. We have been overwhelmed by the generosity and support that has been so freely given.

It is our sincere honor to thank the doctors of North Atlanta Pediatric Associates. Dr. John Knox, Dr. Susan Harrell, Dr. Phil Weiss, Dr. Tama Fuller, and Dr. Elizabeth LeDuc.

We would also like to thank the following families for their specific contributions and enthusiasm.

Janet Schultz and Oscar Olin
Shirley Verwers
Denise and Dominic Mazzone
The Cline Family
James Adams
Kim Stokes
Stephen and Lynne Olin
Sharon Box
Tracy and Marcus Griffin
Laura and Patrick Tate
Brantley and Jon Abrams
Hope and Mike Hargadon
Pamela Ledford-Dyer
Gwen and Mark Brague
The family at The Restoration Church of North Atlanta
Amy and Lare McCreary
Jared and Wendy Goetz

And of course our loving and talented husbands, Jim and Tim. We would have never made it through this without you.

And last but not least, the eight little darlings that really taught us how to love. Kayla, Allison, Blake, Patrick, Brent, Grayson, Hamilton and Bryce!

This book is dedicated to the memory of Marie Olin. "Grandma, your graciousness and legacy of love will live on in my heart forever."
– Jennifer

... and to the memory of Lorraine Adams - "Mom, you helped form me into the woman I am today and I love you."
- Laura

Mom-to-Mom Testimonials

"I just wanted to let you know that Haley has been sleeping from 10:00 p.m. until 5:00 a.m. almost every night, then she goes back to bed until 7:00 a.m. We are so thankful that we were given your name!!! We will certainly pass it along to EVERYONE we know."
—Tina & Drew B.

"Avery has been pretty much sleeping through the night. She sleeps somewhere between 10:00-10:30 p.m. and gets up anywhere between 5:00-6:00 a.m. There are some days where she wakes up at 4:00 a.m., but these aren't as common. She's such a happy baby and I'm grateful your tips have helped me to enjoy Avery that much more."
—Tina F.

"The confidence she has in what she does has helped my husband and I feel that confidence with our own child. It is my wish that every expectant parent whom you encounter reads this right away!"
—Hope H.

"Zachary is doing very well. I still can't believe what a miracle worker you are. I tell everyone, we wouldn't have made it without you (or at least we would have been very sleep deprived). He sleeps 12 hours a night. What a lifesaver!! I just flip through your book for the

answers. Plus, I think just showing us all it really takes is a lot of love and a little discipline, has helped guide us."
—Karin S.

"It was unbelievable how rested she was the next day. That swaddle really helped her to sleep! She was so calm and happy, like a different baby altogether."
—Katherine C.

Additional comments from parents

"The most valuable part was guiding us into a nighttime routine for Faith. The bathing technique is wonderful and soothes our little one every night as we prepare her for bed. We have learned that the more secure and comforted a child feels, the more they will sleep. She gave us great tips on how to calm our baby when she is fussy; to us these tips are invaluable."

"My child is just two months old, she has slept on average from 9:30 p.m. until 6-7 a.m. the next morning! My husband and I pinch ourselves almost every morning in disbelief. Our feeling is that if the parents are HAPPY and RESTED the child will be happy and rested too!"

b

Table of Contents

1

Introduction

Hi, we are Laura Hunter LPN and Jennifer Walker RN BSN, two moms and pediatric nurses who decided it was time to write a how-to childcare book that moms could really use; a book and DVD series by moms and for moms that addressed reality. No psychobabble, not the exhaustive book of disorders that could cause immediate anxiety in the calmest of mothers. No: something different. Something we knew moms needed.

How did we know? Well, between us, we are raising 8 children: two girls (thank you Laura), two sets of twin boys and two singleton boys. We did so, without nannies, night nurses, live in family, and rarely even the occasional babysitter. Now, the clincher here is what we did to help earn enough money to be home during the day to enjoy each and every sloppy meal and stay home at night to snuggle up to whichever child had the current virus that was going around the school.

Like we mentioned, we are pediatric nurses. Not only pediatric nurses, but nurses on call. Which means, that when the busy 9,000-patient pediatric office was closed and moms had questions after hours; they paged us. So from 5 p.m. to 8:30 a.m. every weekday and all weekend the pager went off and every worry and need that any mom was experiencing about her child, be it medical or otherwise...we answered. And this is what we have been doing for the past several years.

After about the 300th call about basic infant care, Laura specifically decided she had to do something better to help teach these new moms how to care for their infants. So she decided to do infant care consultations. We developed a packet of information and instructions for new parents. Then, Laura went into parent's homes and had a 2½ hour consultation in which she went over much of what you will see in the accompanying DVD. After the first consult, we knew that this is what God had purposed in our hearts. Testimonial after testimonial from pleased parents came pouring in. Laura did no advertising, except an ill-placed flier on the check-in counter at the office and she was as busy as she could possibly manage.

Now, the bulk of our clientele was well read in the art of childcare. With each book they read, they hoped to find a secret or a formula that would magically make them amazing and confident parents. As we all know, that did not happen. What did happen was confused and conflicted anxious new parents appeared on our caller I.D. in search of something better; which they found. Then they told two friends, and so on and so on. So, here we are at the result of the popular demand for the real story. Together, we developed this need-to-know manual that shares the realities of parenting.

Laura and I have answered thousands of questions from moms. A typical day at the office in the winter generally runs over 100 calls. After hours in the winter we may field

25-50. So, we know what moms worry about. We know what moms worry about at 9 a.m. We know what moms worry about at 4 p.m. We know what moms worry about at 8 p.m. and we definitely know what moms worry about at 2 in the morning. (The most popular questions are about vomiting, cough and fever. Fussy babies coming in a solid fourth.) We know because the pager goes off, and we know because we have our own children. We have thought some of the same thoughts, and we have felt some of the same feelings.

There is a common fear of doing the wrong thing or making the wrong choice. When this baby is born, it is like a new part of your heart blossomed that you never knew was even there. This concept is impossible to explain; it can only be felt. We have been there. I (Jennifer) was so nervous with baby #1, Grayson, that it was all I could do to leave him in the care of his incredibly capable and loving grandmother. So, we have felt the sting of leaving baby #1 to go to work. That first day is a heartbreaker, and we suffered through it. By the time both of our twins came along, working outside the home was no longer a feasible option. Taking call from home was a great compromise. Difficult, yes, but it has allowed us to interact with other moms in a way only another mom can, with a heart of compassion and understanding.

We did *not* do everything "right" with all our kids. We learned along the way, just like everyone else. We learned about the reality of parenting. And we, too, read the popular baby books. We got particularly frustrated when the

iii

advice assumed that there was only one child in the household, or that parents only have to deal with one child at a time. Most of the books left us feeling overwhelmed. It seemed as if they promised some instant fix that never came. So, if you are looking for a false sense of perfection, you will not find it here. What you will hopefully find here, is a succinct, easy-to-read reference guide.

One concept that we developed has been amazingly successful and that is the "How to get your baby to sleep through the night" information. Over one hundred families have used these techniques and called or wrote us to express how much they appreciated the effectiveness of the information. We feel that watching the "Bedtime and Bath time" routines on the DVD will really make a difference for your family as well.

Children are amazing and wonderful creatures, full of mysteries and wonder. We desire to use our experience and education to help you enjoy the treasure or treasures that God has so graciously given you. He thought you were the best parent for this child/children. You may not have a degree or even a good role model, but He chose you. We want to help equip you with some of the information that we know moms need. This book or DVD will not make you a perfect parent, but perhaps we can help you enjoy the ride.

Receiving instruction about basic baby care can help decrease parental anxieties. However, there is so much more to learn, each and every day. We truly have a heart for parents, moms in particular, and we desire to provide the food that your family needs to flourish. We want to provide inspiration, not condemnation. This is the heart of God.

Now, the information in this book and DVD has helped so many parents to enjoy and understand their babies as evidenced by the glowing testimonials. And remember, they are simply enjoying the parenting process better. We have not magically made them perfect parents. With that in mind, may this journey, bless and enrich your life, helping you to enjoy the first six months of your baby's life. And while we are at it, we hope to clue you in on what to do with this baby when you get home from the hospital.

This is the condensed, anxiety free version of proper childcare techniques. And in it you will find excerpts of real calls that we frequently get from our actual patients. (Names excluded of course!) So, feel free to use the following pages as guidelines for proper baby care.

How to Use Book One

There was once a time when mothers taught their daughters the ins and outs of childcare. In this day and age, with medical research evolving so fast and the family unit being dispersed both far and wide, it is rare to find a family that is able to get all of their questions answered in that manner. That is where we come in. We have created the DVD included in this book to help show you how to perform some basic infant care tasks. The tasks we selected are ones that are hard to explain with the written word, and more easily learned through demonstration. What a concept! Your own Pediatric nurse to actually demonstrate how to do the complicated stuff! The skills that are essential to the success of a good night's sleep and more are as follows:

- o Swaddling
- o Bath time routine
- o Bedtime routine
- o Frustration
- o The Three Day Rule
- o Nasal Suctioning
- o Massaging Tear Ducts
- o Taking a rectal temperature
- o Nail clipping
- o Diapering

You will get so much more out of these materials if you watch the DVD and follow along in this guidebook. Enjoy!

 **The swaddling techniques that are so essential for newborns, use a special size blanket made of a flannel material that only stretches in one direction. More blankets are available at www.momsoncall.com. The dimensions of this blanket are 44x44 inches. If you know someone who has a sewing machine that has surging capabilities, you may make extras yourself. The standard size flannel blanket that is sold in stores will not provide an effective tight swaddle in the fashion that we are showing you. We have also found that other swaddling techniques do not hold as well as what we have developed. It is crucial to correctly swaddle.

Seeking medical care whenever you are concerned is recommended by Moms on Call.

Any time that you are concerned, or notice any symptoms, call your Pediatrician's office. Sometimes babies have discreet symptoms like a fever, and other times there is just something that you can't explain, call it mother's intuition or a nagging feeling that something may be wrong. Those are both valid reasons to seek medical attention. Many of the concepts addressed in this book and DVD vary from Pediatrician to Pediatrician. When it comes to your child's care, you are responsible for making the final decisions.

SECTION ONE:
THE BASICS

WHAT EVERY MOM NEEDS TO KNOW ABOUT BASIC INFANT CARE

"Keep sound wisdom and discretion: so they will be life to your soul and grace to your neck."

Proverbs 3:21b-22

GENERAL SHOPPING LIST

Moms on Call LLC recommends having the following items on hand prior to needing them. This will cut down on any middle of the night trips to the pharmacy after you speak to the Pediatrician's office. These items are the ones that we have in our own closets and diaper bags. So, if you want to know what two Pediatric nurses with eight kids keep in the medicine cabinet, this is it!

- o Infant Tylenol - (1 bottle) and Children's Tylenol Suspension (2-3 bottles)
- o Fever-All Suppositories (Tylenol in suppository form)
- o Children's Ibuprofen (Motrin/Advil) for use in babies over 6 months of age. (2-3 bottles)
- o Benadryl Liquid - for use in babies over 14 pounds and over 4 months old. (2-3 bottles)
- o Triaminic Nighttime Cold and Cough (purple) (1 bottle)
- o Robitussin PE - (1 bottle)
- o Vicks 44M
- o Normal Saline nose drops (Little noses is our favorite-get the plain drops.)
- o Vitamin A&D Ointment
- o Vaseline
- o Lotrimen AF (may find in foot care section of the pharmacy)
- o Diaper rash Cream (Palmer's is one without zinc oxide. You can find it at

Babies-R-Us)
- Aqua-Phor Healing Ointment (should be able to find in diaper section of store)
- Regular Kitchen Cornstartch.
- Aveeno Oatmeal Bath Packets
- Eucerin or Lubriderm lotion
- Cortaid Hyrdrocortisone Cream
- Hydrogen Peroxide (2-3 smaller bottles)
- Polysporin Antibiotic Ointment
- Anti-Bacterial hand wash
- 4x4 Gauze - individually packed - (2-3 boxes)
- 2x2 Gauze individually packed -(2-3 boxes)
- Band-aids
- Ace Bandages (2-3 rolls)
- Squeezable ice packs
- Tweezers (diagonal head) (2-3)
- Glycerin Suppositories
- Baby pear or white grape juice
- Isomil DF (Anti-diarrhea formula)
- Pedialyte (electrolyte replenisher)
- Pedialyte popsicles
- Canned peaches in Heavy Syrup
- B-D Digital Thermometer (2-3)
- K-Y Jelly
- Medicine Dosage Syringes
- Infant Gas Drops
- Bug Repellant (Skintastic is one particular brand. Spray on hands then apply to infant sparingly, or just put repellant on baby's clothes and socks.)
- Sunscreen (Water Babies or Spectra by Coopertone are our favorites. May use on infants but remember no longer than 10 minutes in direct sunlight. If you are

sweating, it is too warm for baby.
- o Nail Clippers by Safety First with the white handgrip
- o Long Handled infant spoons (usually one piece of plastic)
- o Biz Laundry Soap (Great for stain removal - especially if items are soaked overnight.)

Note: Do not administer any medications to your baby without consulting your Pediatrician.

BATHING

CALL "Yes, I have a one week old and I wasn't sure if I could bathe her in her little bath now, or if I should wait until the umbilical cord falls off?"

This is a frequently asked question. Your baby likely will have their first bath at home. It is unbelievably fun and adorable but be careful - wet babies are slippery! Support baby's head until he/she can do so on their own. See below:

- Until the umbilical cord falls off, sponge bath no soap, water is tepid (slightly warmer than room temperature)
- After the umbilical cord falls off, regular baths may be given. (Baby soap is optional but it sure makes them smell good!)

Always make sure that all supplies are kept within arms reach. A basket of items is an easy way to ensure that everything is kept together.

You may use an infant bathtub or hold the baby carefully in the regular tub. Use non-skid mats and always be cautious to support the baby's head and neck.

Only fill the bath with 1-2 inches of water. Never leave your baby/babies in the tub or around water unattended.

Things to have at arm's reach in the bathroom:
- o Towels
- o Washcloths
- o Baby soap
- o Soft baby brush

Bathing every day is fine, but during the first few months 2-3 times/week is enough for a full bath. Always rinse your baby well. Babies associate bath time with bedtime. At the very least, sponge the baby down as a nighttime routine.

Note: The DVD demonstration of bathing techniques will be quite helpful.

Females—Do not wash female genital areas with soap. Rinse with plain water and wipe from front to back. *Tip: Spread the labia (lip-like parts) and clean with a diaper wipe or washcloth when taking diaper off PRIOR to bath.*
Males (circumcised)—After the circumcision is healed, gently pull skin back so lip of penis is seen all the way around and clean well.
Males (uncircumcised)—Clean the foreskin well. No need to retract the skin during the first year of life. Speak with your doctor for specific care.

Shampooing hair: Apply baby shampoo to hair. Scrub scalp with soft infant brush. If you are concerned about hurting the soft spot, just scrub gently. Rinse hair well.

Umbilical Cord Care: Keep cord dry. Lift up and apply alcohol with a Q-tip around the base of the cord. Do this at least 2-3 times a day until it falls off. You may want to cut out a wedge in the diaper so the cord is not covered.
Signs to watch for:
- o Strong foul odor (trust us, it finds you).
- o Bleeding that runs out of the belly-button (more than one teaspoon bright red blood.) Dried blood is okay. The blood that is in the cord is left over maternal blood, it is generally not the baby's blood. If the cord has bright red or even persistent dried blood, the Pediatrician can usually fix it by putting on a special compound that is painless for baby.
- o Oozing yellow/whitish discharge

BOWEL MOVEMENTS

CALL "My baby is three weeks old and has not had a stool for almost 24 hours!!!"

Can you believe how we obsess over our baby's bowel movements? Color, consistency, frequency and amount of apparent straining are common concerns for moms. Let us set your mind at ease. There is a wide range of what is considered normal for a bowel movement.

After the first week of life, if you are lucky, bowel movements slow down from every feeding to maybe once or twice a day, and even once a week for some two and three month olds. (If you are not lucky, your twins have simultaneous and copious stools eight times a day each until they are three years old. That's sixteen poopy diapers per day between them - Jennifer!) Now, let's carry on.

Color
- o Breastfed: generally yellow seedy, can vary from yellowish brown to green.
- o Formula fed: darker in color, can vary from yellow to brown to green.

Note: The color of stools will vary from feeding to feeding, generally according to what the baby's body is absorbing and/or excreting.

Call Pediatrician's office if:
- More than 1 teaspoon bright red blood at any time.
- Less than 1 teaspoon bright red blood x 3 or more stools.
- Black tarry stools
- What looks like coffee ground material.
- Fluorescent green. (We mean almost glows in the dark.)
- Clay colored stool for more than 2 weeks.

Frequency
- Breastfed—May vary greatly. Early on, the baby may be stooling every feeding, from small amounts to full diapers. May be watery to mushy. Then at 4-6 weeks old may begin decreasing, varying from every feeding to one large bowel movement every 7 days.
- Formula fed—Will vary greatly. May be 3-4 bowel movements a day to one every other day or so. Occasionally may go several days without a bowel movement. Stool consistency may be mushy to firm.

Constipation: True constipation is a term used to describe hard, pebble-like stools. There is a difference between constipation and infrequent stooling. Infrequent stoolers are gassy and have a soft large bowel movement every 3-7 days.

Signs of Constipation
- o Painful passage of stools when the stool itself is hard and pebble-like.
- o Abdomen distention but remains relatively soft
- o Decreased appetite.

Note: Remember, babies commonly grunt, push, strain, draw up legs, and turn red when passing a stool. This is normal. Think about what you would do if you had to have a bowel movement while laying down. After the 2nd month or so, many breast-fed babies pass normal, large, soft bowel movements at infrequent intervals up to one every 7 days. This is generally not abnormal as long as it is not hard and painful.

Relief Measures if your Pediatrician diagnoses constipation:
- o In babies, you may stimulate with a rectal thermometer or Q-tip with Vaseline or K-Y Jelly. Insert ¼ inch into rectum and rotate Q-tip a few times.
- o Glycerin suppositories are available over-the-counter. They are made of sugar-

water and do not have any medications in them. They just stimulate the bowels to move.
o May give fruit juice to infants 4 weeks old twice a day. We recommend Gerber if approved by your Pediatrician (Pear, White Grape or Apple- 1-2 ounces in a separate bottle a.m. and p.m.)
o Babies more than 4 months old may have strained baby food with baby cereals; such as apricots, prunes, peaches, pears, plums, beans, peas, or spinach at least 2 times per day. Avoid carrots, squash, bananas, or apples.

Your Pediatrician can recommend a stool softener to be taken for approximately a week. However, stool softeners are generally not used in babies under six months old.

When to seek medical care
o No relief after trying above.
o Abdominal tenderness when pressing on either side of bellybutton.
o Fever—ask your Pediatrician for a fever handout.
o Happens frequently.
o Persistent vomiting. (See vomiting section.)

12

Infrequent Stoolers: Signs
- o Soft stools: can be every other day to once every 7 days
- o May have increased gas and/or fussiness.

Relief measures for infrequent stoolers: (only if the baby seems uncomfortable and with the approval of your Pediatrician).
- o Rectal stimulation every other day if uncomfortable.
- o Increase fluids (breastmilk or formula) - or can add 1-2 ounces of water per day
- o Mylicon gas drops.
- o Glycerin suppository OTC (over the counter)

DIARRHEA

Diarrhea can be caused by a gastrointestinal virus that generally lasts 5-7 days. However, sometimes babies over 3 months old may have a day of diarrhea secondary to mild stomach irritation, and this will pass in one or two days.

Signs: More than 5 watery stools in a 24-hour period.
- Relief measures—we do not like to give medication that claims to stop diarrhea for infants or kids under 2 years old. This is because most diarrhea is caused by a gastrointestinal virus that will run its course. We want the diarrhea to get out of the baby's system. This is the body's natural way of handling this kind of virus. If your baby is having diarrhea, contact your Pediatrician.

Infants
- Formula Fed—may switch to Isomil DF for a few days.
- Breast-Fed—Continue to breastfeed. Breast milk is the gentlest thing for an infant's tummy.
- Baby food for a baby more than 6

14

months old. Baby foods that are starchy are good choices i.e. cereal, applesauce, bananas, carrots, mashed potatoes.

When to seek medical care
- o 8 or more watery stools a day for 5 days.
- o Blood or mucous in stool.
- o Fever (ask your Pediatrician for a fever hand-out)
- o Abdominal tenderness/hard at rest.
- o **Any signs of dehydration:**
  - o Longer than 6 hours without urinating.
  - o No tears when crying.
  - o Inside of lips feel dry when you swipe your pinky finger along the inside of bottom lip.
  - o Sunken soft spot.
  - o Increased lethargy.

Note: Diarrhea is very contagious. All family members need to wash hands well after changing diapers and/or using the toilet.

EYE DRAINAGE

> **CALL** "My baby has a thin mucous discharge from one eye. Some mornings the eye has goo on it and it is a little sticky."

Watery eyes or discharge that is clear to yellow in color, may come and go until 6 months of age. Your Pediatrician may diagnose a blocked tear duct. The tube that normally carries tears from the tear duct to the eye is blocked. It is very common. If your baby is having discharge, contact your Pediatrician's office during office hours.

Care: Wash your hands! Clean the baby's face with a warm, not hot, washcloth and then, using your pinky finger, massage (where the eye meets the bridge of the nose) in a circular motion while applying pressure. DO NOT APPLY DIRECT PRESSURE TO THE EYE ITSELF.

When to seek medical care:
o Thick yellow or green discharge that reappears after wiping away several times a day.
o No improvement of symptoms with massage and warm compress in 3-4 days.
o Eye redness or swelling
o **Seek immediate medical attention for a baby under 3 months old with a rectal temperature 100.4 F or higher**

FEVER

CALL "I think my baby has fever, but I am too scared to take a rectal temperature."

We get so many calls about fever. This is a misunderstood symptom. Our bodies are designed to fight off infection. One way that the body does that is to turn up the heat when a virus or bacteria is detected, hoping the bacteria or virus will not want to stick around if it gets too hot. So, mild fevers in babies **over 3 months old** can be quite beneficial.

It is also imperative that you are able to take an accurate temperature, especially in babies under 3 months old, because a fever of 100.4 F. or higher is considered an emergency in that age group. Babies do not feel particularly warm when their temperature is only 100.4. When taking the baby's temperature, we recommend taking rectal temperatures exclusively until the baby is over 18 months old. That is the most accurate way to take a temperature. The ear thermometers, forehead thermometers and pacifier thermometers are just not as accurate in infants. We recommend using a B-D Digital Thermometer.

In infants-normal rectal temperatures are between 97-100.3 degrees F. Temperatures may vary according to several factors, including activity level and times of day.

17

Taking a Rectal Temperature
1. Lubricate the thermometer with a pea-sized amount of Vaseline or K-Y Jelly.
2. Lay infant on back as if changing a diaper.
3. Lift legs so rectum is easily seen.
4. Press button on thermometer to turn it on.
5. Insert thermometer into rectum about ½ inch or until you can no longer see the silver tip of the thermometer.
6. Hold thermometer in place 3 minutes or until it beeps.
7. Remove and read thermometer.

Treatment
- o In babies 3-6 months old, may use Tylenol according to package directions, every 4 hours but not more than 6 doses in 24 hours.
- o **If over 6 months old**, if irritable or fussy and/or not resting well, may alternate Tylenol and Ibuprofen every 3 hours as needed. (i.e. 3 a.m. - Tylenol, 6 a.m. - Motrin, 9 a.m. -Tylenol, 12 p.m. - Motrin. And so on.)
- o Extra fluids

When to seek medical care
- o **Seek immediate medical attention for a baby under 3 months old with a rectal temperature 100.4 F or higher**
- o A baby between 3 and 6 months old with a temperature more than 101.5 rectally- call the Pediatrician

Note: Tylenol or Motrin do not cure the cause of the fever. It is for comfort only. Once these medications wear off, the fever will come back until they are no longer sick. Often the fever will not come all the way back down to normal, even with the fever control medicine. It can hover between 101-102 rectally in an infant over 3 months even with fever control medicines.

Note: Each individual Pediatrician can have varied guidelines on fever management. Ask your Pediatrician for a "Fever Handout". This will help you to know what treatments they recommend and when they want you to call their office.

Also, we would like to clarify that babies over 3 months can generally take Tylenol but babies have to be at least 6 months to take Ibuprofen products like Motrin or Advil.

NAIL CLIPPING

> **CALL** "I can't get my baby's finger nails clipped. I'm too nervous that I might cut off the end of her finger. She keeps moving around so much."

Trim nails after a bath, when the nails are soft. This may take two people or do when infant is asleep.

- o Trim toenails straight across to prevent ingrown toenails. You will not need to cut toenails as often as fingernails.
- o When cutting fingernails, round off corners to minimize the chance of your infant scratching him or herself.

Tip: Use nail clippers that have a white handgrip.

Note: See the DVD segment on "Nail Clipping" to watch an excellent method for getting your baby's nailed trimmed.

NASAL CONGESTION

CALL "I have a 3 week old infant with a stuffy nose. I think she caught my cold."

It can be normal for infants to have nasal congestion as long as there is no cough or rectal temperature of 100.4 F or higher. We even have a term for it amazingly called... infant congestion.

Relief measures if approved by your Pediatrician.
- o Use saline nose drops. Instill 2-3 drops in each nostril, allow to sit a couple of seconds. Use bulb syringe. Depress bulb, hold one nostril closed, insert tip in open nostril, at the same time slowly remove bulb syringe, while releasing the suction of the bulb and doing a sweeping motion in nostril. The first 2 days may use 3-4 times per day then drop to 2-3 times per day. Preferably before meals and before bed. (See DVD)
- o Temperature in home: Winter 68-70 degrees; Summer 72-74 degrees
- o Dress the infant as you would dress yourself, as far as layering and seasonal appropriateness. If you are wearing long pants and a long sleeve shirt, then baby should be in long baby pants and a long sleeve baby shirt. May use a short-sleeve onsie underneath.

- May use a cool mist humidifier.
- Elevate head of bed. Do not place any objects in baby's crib. May prop one end of mattress up by placing a rolled up regular sized towel underneath one end of the mattress. Do not exceed a 20 degree angle.

When to seek medical care
- Frequent cough with no improvement after doing above. Frequent=several times/hour.
- Chest sinking in when breathing. Ribs pronounced during inhale.
- Nostrils flaring
- Wheezing (whistle or squeaking sound)
- Stridor - noise made on inhale when not coughing-tight sounding.
- Breathing faster then 60 respirations/minute.
- **Seek immediate medical attention for a baby under 3 months old with a rectal temperature 100.4 F or higher**
- Call Pediatrician if temperature is more than 101.5 in a baby between 3 and 6 months old.

SKIN CARE

CALL "My baby has these pink bumps on her face and chest, no fever, and she acts fine and we have pictures scheduled for tomorrow."

It is very seldom that you see a baby with perfect skin. Expect skin rashes and call your pediatrician when they occur. They may diagnose your baby with one of these common skin rashes.

TYPES OF COMMON SKIN RASHES

Baby acne: small red bumps on face, chest, scalp and back. Usually begins at 2-4 weeks and can last until 4-6 months.
- Clean with mild soap and water, no need to apply lotions or baby oils. Can come and go for several weeks.

Drool Rash: Pink splotchy area on the chin or cheeks that comes and goes. Can be caused by spitting up, pacifiers that hold drool against skin, or frequent drooling.
- Rinse baby's face with water after feeds.
- Vaseline on area to protect skin from irritation.

Heat rash: pin-prickly pink bumps and splotchy areas. Can be seen on skin that touches mom's skin during breastfeeding or along the back where baby sweats in the car seat.

- o Change your baby's position during feeding.
- o Use cornstarch powder (not baby powder) to back or chest. Put powder in your hand first, then apply to area. Be careful not to get powder or dispenser anywhere near the baby's face, as infants can choke on the powder.

Milia: tiny white bumps that occur on the face, nose, forehead, chin, and cheeks. Usually will disappear by 1-2 months of age.

- o Do not apply any ointments or creams to these.

Dry flaky skin: May use Eucerin or Lubriderm to moisturize skin. Dry patches may occur behind knees and elbows, although it may also appear in other areas such as cheeks, diaper area, or face. Any flaky skin in the fatty folds of the wrists or ankles can be left alone.

- o Apply 1% Hydrocortisone cream minimally twice a day as long as your Pediatrician recommends it. If that does not clear up in three days or gets worse at any time, call your Pediatrician.

Wet moist areas: under neck, in skin folds. May use cornstarch to help with moisture. See above.

Note: Any blisters containing clear fluid or pimples containing pus which occur in the first month of life, or any rash accompanied by a fever must be seen by the Pediatrician.

Cradle Cap: oily yellow scales on scalp. Begins first few weeks of life and can last several weeks.

- o To help prevent cradle cap, shampoo hair with soap and scrub with soft infant brush. Rinse well.
- o If already present, wash hair with Neutrogena T-gel if approved by your Pediatrician. (Remember to keep out of eyes) Apply to hair and scrub lightly with infant hairbrush. Do this 3 times a week. Once clear, use mild infant soap for shampooing. Do not use T-gel for more than 2 weeks. If symptoms last longer than 2 weeks or worsen with treatment then the baby needs to be seen by the Pediatrician.
- o If severe crustiness, put some baby oil on the scalp one hour before washing to soften the crust. Make sure to rinse well.

Diaper rash

- **Redness.** No diaper wipes (use wet washcloth or soft paper towels). Leave open to air, may use diaper cream (Vitamin A&D, Aquaphor, Gerber, Palmer's, Desitin.) Also, may use kitchen cornstarch to keep moisture from irritating the skin. Change diapers frequently.

- **Red and bumpy.** No diaper wipes, leave open to air. Change frequently. Apply Lotrimen AF three times a day if approved by your Pediatrician, and follow with any above diaper cream and kitchen cornstarch. Use for 7 days. If bleeding or no improvement in 3-4 days, then see your Pediatrician.

Tip: Laura likes to use a combination of Aqua-Phor and Palmer's mixed together then apply cornstarch. We also recommend Kirkland's Diaper Wipes at Costco. They do not leave any residue and are gentle on the skin. You can also buy these in bulk, which is good because you will use more than you think.

Note: If no redness or irritation, no need to use diaper rash cream.

ORAL CARE/TEETHING

> **CALL** "My baby is so fussy. I am wondering if she is teething or has an ear infection?"

There is no way to definitively tell whether or not your baby has an ear infection unless the doctor looks in the ear. That said, ear infections are rare in the first 3 months of life.

Teething generally begins between 3 months and one year of age. Some children do not have any pain while teething. We would find that our kids would often try to put their entire fist in their mouth. And look out if your hand or chin got too close, because they would try to gnaw on anything that got within biting distance!

Signs
- o Increased drooling
- o Chewing constantly
- o Swollen, red gums

Usually the teeth break through in the following order:
- o 2 lower incisors
- o 4 upper incisors
- o 2 lower incisors and all 4 first molars.
- o 4 canines
- o 4 second molars

Remember no two children are alike.

Relief Measures:
- o Massage swollen gums
- o An infant washcloth, wet it slightly and put it in the freezer for 10 minutes. Allow them to chew on it as needed.
- o Give Tylenol as needed for mild discomfort if older than 3 months and approved by Pediatrician.

Note: It is very difficult to tell the difference between teething and ear pain. If running a fever more than 2-3 days, not sleeping well, grabbing at ears and has cold symptoms, your baby should be seen in the office.

Dental Care at/after 3 months of age
- o Begin brushing teeth/gums with wet gauze or washcloth wrapped around your index finger. Be careful not to let the gauze slip off your finger.
- o There is no need for toothpaste until they are able to spit it out.
- o Never allow your child to go to sleep with milk/formula residue on their gums/teeth. This causes painful tooth decay. That means no bottles in the crib!
- o When you begin using toothpaste only use a pea-sized amount.
- o You need to help your child brush their teeth until they are around 6 years old.
- o Begin flossing when the molars start to touch each other.

The first visit to the dentist should be around 2-3 years old. Earlier if noticeable tooth decay or problems, including chipped teeth. We recommend a Pediatric Dentist because they generally know how to deal with the unique problems that can arise for kids. Be aware that most Pediatric Dentists will have you sit in the waiting room while your child is treated. Your child will tolerate procedures much better without you. Moms often are so anxious that it makes it difficult to calm the child.

Thrush: White irregular shaped patches that coat the inside of the mouth and sometimes the tongue (if only on tongue may not be thrush). The coating cannot be wiped off with your fingernail. May cause mild discomfort when eating. Call office if you suspect thrush.

- o Nystatin oral suspension can usually be called into the pharmacy if your doctor's office suspects thrush.
- o Boil all bottle nipples and pacifiers. Also wipe down baby toys that come in contact with the mouth with a germicidal cloth and rinse thoroughly. Do this for the first three days of treatment.
- o If breastfeeding, apply Nystatin to irritated areas of nipples with your OB/GYN's approval. Also clean your nipples with vinegar washes after every feeding and let air dry (one part vinegar to two parts water).

When to seek medical care

- o If no improvement after doing Nystatin for 7 days.
- o The thrush gets worse instead of better.
- o Discomfort continues after doing treatment for 3-4 days.

SECTION TWO: ROUTINE ISSUES

FEEDING INFORMATION AND HOW TO GET YOUR BABY TO SLEEP THROUGH THE NIGHT!!!

"When wisdom enters your heart, and knowledge is pleasant to your soul, discretion will preserve you; understanding will keep you"
Proverbs 2:10-11

TWINS

Call "I am a mother of twins and I am so exhausted. One of the babies wants to eat every 2 hours and the other every three. I feel like I am feeding them around the clock."

Here are the survival tactics that helped us:

1. **If one baby eats, they both eat-period.** Even if one twin does not appear hungry, feed that one, anyway. Keep them on the exact same schedule and we mean it! It is okay to put them both in bouncy seats and feed them simultaneously with bottles. Just remember to talk softly to both of them and give them each a few minutes of your full attention. Breast-feeders can hold both babies in the football hold and feed at the same time.

(Jennifer- I did not like the way simultaneous breastfeeding felt and decided to breastfeed one baby and bottle feed the other. Then at the next feeding, whoever bottle fed last time was the breast feeder and the other got the bottle. I would breastfeed the one baby in the cradle hold while holding a bottle in the other baby's mouth with my "free" hand. The baby with the bottle was generally propped up on a nearby bouncy seat or Boppie pillow. This way they both were getting at least half breast milk every day. And they were fed, burped and changed in 45 minutes).

It is also good to allow Dad to feed the babies sometimes, whether that is in the middle of night, or one feeding during the day while you nap. He can feed both with pumped breast milk from a bottle or formula. It gives Dad a chance to have that much needed interaction.

2. When one baby sleeps, the other does also. Naptimes and bedtimes are the same. (See #4 for specific guidelines for "Bedtime") Again, one baby may not seem sleepy at the same time as the other. This is survival mode. They will learn to be on the same schedule. This is part of learning to live in a family environment. One twin may have to learn to sleep more to accommodate the family schedule.

Some parents like to stagger the naptimes so they have an hour to spend with one baby at a time. Once they get to 4 or 5 months old, this is fine. The feeding and changing schedules prior to that time are entirely too time consuming (unless you have helpers, like a night nurse, nanny or live in family member).

3. Use your helpers. In the first two or three months you will be absolutely exhausted. If grandma comes for a visit one day, allow her to watch the babies while you nap for an hour or two. If neighbors or friends ask how they can help, allow them to make a meal or arrange for household chores. Many people would love to help if they just had a tangible thing to do. Let others make meals for you. If someone you trust offers to baby-sit, say "That sounds great, when are you available?" The first few months of twins is not the time to let your pride step in the way of your sanity! Think of it this way, the more you allow others to help, the more time you will have to actually enjoy your twins!

4. Use the Moms on Call Method of getting your baby to sleep. As early as 5 weeks old, your babies can be bathed, fed, swaddled and sleeping 5-9 hours per night. (However, we do not recommend swaddling babies over 4 months old.) This will make the hectic days so much easier. We do realize that some moms do not have the extra hands around at night. Also, single parents of twins are more likely to have to do the "Bath time" and "Bedtime" routines alone. So, here is a way to do the "Bath time" and "Bedtime" routines if you are alone.

Put both babies in the bouncy seat in the bathroom. Give them a bath, one at a time. While one takes a bath, the other waits and may cry or fuss. Once they are both bathed and both sitting in their towels in the bouncy seats, take them one at a time (bouncy seat and all) to get dressed in the nursery. Put the first baby to get dressed back in the bouncy seat momentarily while you dress the other baby. So, when they are both dressed and back in the bouncy seats in the nursery, play soft music; feed them their last nighttime feeding (don't forget to burp them) then swaddle each of them securely. Place them in the crib in their foam positioners; turn on the white noise and turn off the lights. The babies can sleep in the same crib or separate cribs. They can even have their own room, if you have the space. Take your cues from them. (Laura - My boys would sleep head-to-head every night. If we put them on opposite sides of the crib, by morning they were head-to-head. They are three years old now and still wake up head-to-head every morning.)

5. Remember, it gets easier as they get older. Twins are incredibly labor intensive for the first three years. Double the work, but double the love! The great news is that they will hit a period of time when they are continuous playmates. It is easier to have two 18 month olds, because you are not their only source of entertainment. They will play together and keep each other amused for years. It is wonderful. (Jennifer – My mom is a twin and she described it this way: "Having a twin is not like having another brother or sister, it's like having another you.")

BREASTFEEDING

CALL "I am worried that my baby is not getting enough."

Many breastfeeding moms share this common concern. We cannot measure in ounces, how much breast milk a baby swallows each feeding. However, we do have some guidelines that are helpful in determining if the baby is getting the breast milk they need.

Is she getting enough?
- o Nursing at least 8 times in 24 hours. May drop down to 6-7 times around 4-8 weeks old. Longer stretches at night are acceptable.
- o Is satisfied after nursing.
- o Urinates at least every other feeding.
- o Gains approximately a half an ounce a day for the first few weeks (with the exception of week 1 when newborns commonly loose weight).
- o Inside of bottom lip is smooth and moist.
- o Soft spot is not markedly sunken.
- o Periods of alertness that last at least 20-30 minutes several times a day.
- o Let-down reflex is present for mom.

How often? How long?
- o The first 1-2 weeks, nurse on demand. Thereafter, every 2½-3

hours is sufficient during the day. At night, may go longer, as much as 5-6 hours as long as the baby is healthy and beginning to gain weight.

- o After your milk comes in, usually by the 8th day at the latest, feed as long as your infant wants on the first breast, up to 20 minutes. That ensures your infant is getting the high-fat, calorie-rich hind milk. You can tell they have finished when the sucking slows down and your breast is soft and mushy. Then offer the second breast if he is interested. Remember to alternate which breast you start with at each feeding.

Latching:

- o Rooting reflex: bring baby close to your breast, then stroke the baby's cheek. Your baby will turn their head and open their mouth.
- o Put as much of the areola into the baby's mouth as possible. NEVER allow the baby to suck on nipple only.
- o Holding breast from below will help put the breast into the correct position.
- o Place the baby's body directly facing the breast.
- o If not latched on correctly, remove by placing finger gently on the corner of baby's mouth to break suction. Try above steps again.

Positions
- **Cradle Hold:** Sitting in your lap with baby's head in the crook of your arm. Baby's chest should be against your chest so that they do not have to turn their head to reach your nipple.
- **Lying Down:** Lay on your side and place the baby on their side facing you, with the baby's head at your breast.
- **Football Hold:** Hold your baby like a football along your forearm, with baby's body on your arm and their face toward your breast. Use your other hand to support the position of the baby's head.

Find a relaxed and comfortable position. Change positions with different feedings. Use pillows for your back. (Boppie pillows or other nursing pillows are great. These saved my aching back when I was nursing my twins—Jennifer.)

Nipple Care
- After each feeding, coat nipples with some breast milk.
- Allow nipples to air dry.
- If cracked, apply 100% lanolin to nipples after feedings. (If allergic to wool, do not use lanolin).
- Make sure the infant is latching correctly.
- If sore, begin feeding on the less sore nipple.
- If the pain is severe, may need to pump until nipples heal.

Plugged ducts: hard, tender lump in your breast, caused by incomplete emptying of the

breast milk.
- o Nurse on the tender side first.
- o Massage the breast with the lump, trying to express extra milk.
- o Apply moist heat to breast. Shower or bathe while massaging and expressing extra milk.

Engorgement: large firm and tender breasts. Lasts until your body gets used to making and releasing milk. Once your baby is nursing well and milk is flowing easily, there will be less swelling and firmness.
- o Warm breast before nursing with warm washcloth.
- o Gently massage breast while nursing.
- o Cool washcloths to breast between feedings.
- o Cabbage leaves: Put thoroughly washed and dried crisp cold green cabbage leaves over your engorged breasts. Leave on for 20-30 minutes until leaves are wilted.

If so engorged that it is difficult for baby to latch on, you may need to pump or hand-express some milk before feeding.

Mastitis (Breast infection): Achy, flu-like symptoms, fever, chills, headache, breast pain, breast redness, firmness.
- o Call your physician immediately if you have any of these symptoms.
- o Take all of the antibiotic prescribed.
- o Rest and stay in bed.
- o Drink plenty of fluids.
- o Nurse more often, especially on the side

that is infected.
- o Warm washcloth to breast before feeding.

When to call your OB/GYN:
- o Fever
- o Chills
- o Headache
- o Flu-like symptoms
- o Pain/redness to breast
- o Nipples that sting or burn
- o Shooting pains in your breast during nursing
- o Painful lump

Breastfeeding
Storage and Handling of Breast Milk
- o Wash hands well.
- o Store milk in plastic rather than glass.
- o Label each with the date and time expressed.
- o Storage
  - o May be stored in the refrigerator for 72 hours after pumping.
  - o May be stored in the refrigerator for 24 hours after thawing.
  - o May be stored in freezer (5 degrees Fahrenheit - 15 degrees Fahrenheit) up to 3 months after pumping. Deep freezer (0 degrees Fahrenheit and below) may be stored up to 6 months.

Thawing
- o In refrigerator until no more ice.
- o Under running warm water or in a bowl

of warm water. Make sure the nipple stays above the water line at all times.

- o The 2 ounce plastic bottles often fit nicely into a coffee cup filled ½ way with warm water.
- o Do not thaw milk at room temperature. Bacteria can grow in it.
- o Do not allow thawed milk to sit for more than 2 hours at room temperature.
- o Do not refreeze thawed milk.

Amounts
- o Allow 20-30 minutes to eat. If it takes an hour to feed a healthy infant then it is taking too long. See the lactation consultant.
- o Begin with 2 ounces at a time. Add more until the 30-minute mark. (EXAMPLE: If the baby finishes 3 ounces for two feedings in a row, then have 3½-4 ounces in the bottle for subsequent feedings. This ensures that the baby can eat more if they are hungry.)
- o Never reuse breast milk that is left over in a bottle after one hour.

Vitamins/Supplements
Consult your physician at the 2-month check-up to guide you in vitamin supplementation. Herbs and Homeopathic remedies are usually not tested on infants and children under 6 years old. Therefore we cannot recommend any herbal preparation. That is not to say that they are harmful. There is just not enough information available about their safety when used in children or infants.

Gas in Breastfed infants

- Empty one breast completely before switching breasts.
- Burp well and often.
- May use infant gas drops according to package label. These drops break big air bubbles up into little air bubbles so they are easier to pass. Use before feedings or after feedings.
- Infants make more gas than adults do. It is okay to leave gas untreated.
- Babies get fussy in the evenings. They often draw up their legs and make strange faces. This does not necessarily mean that they are in pain. Again, think of what you would have to do in order to pass gas while lying down.

FORMULA FEEDING

CALL " Yes, I started my baby on Lipil and then he was fussy so I changed him to Isomil. He was still fussy so the next day I tried Carnation Good Start."

One important factor when deciding to change to a new formula is that it takes baby's digestive system 5-7 days to adjust to the new enzymes and sugars in a new formula. Do not switch unless advised by the Pediatrician, and then expect 5-7 days of fussiness, gassiness, and changes in bowel habits.
Brand names of formulas:
o Ross products: Similac, Similac Advanced, Isomil among many others
o Mead-Johnson Products: Enfamil, Enfamil Lipil, Prosobee among many others
o Store-Brands - Wal-Mart, Target, etc.

Note: Formula companies are regulated and formulas are designed to meet the nutritional needs of your infant.

Forms of formulas:
Powder
o Least expensive.
o May be prepared ahead of time.
o May use blender with short pulses, then allow the mixture to sit in the refrigerator for a few hours before serving. Do not serve right away after blending this way or else it's gas city!

o Use warm tap water to mix formula and store in the refrigerator for up to 48 hours. Using tap water ensures the baby is getting some fluoride. In some counties boiling tap water is necessary. If you are on well water, boil your tap water for 5 minutes and then let cool.

Concentrated: Use equal amounts of tap water and formula. Also, this mixture of formula may be stored in the refrigerator for up to 48 hours.

Ready to feed: Most expensive. May use occasionally, but remember that ready to feed formulas do not contain any fluoride.

How much? How long?
o Newborns will usually eat 2-3 ounces every 3 hours, or six to eight feedings per day, for the first three weeks. Then 5-6 feeding per day from 1-3 months, and 4-5 feedings per day from 3-7 months. Then drop to 3-4 feedings/day from 7-9 months.
o A feeding should not take longer than 30 minutes
o The amount of formula can vary from feeding to feeding and day to day. Some days they need more and some less, just like us. Between 24-32 ounces of formula a day is generally sufficient for healthy babies.
o Never reuse formula left in a bottle for

over an hour.

Amounts
- o Has 20-30 minutes to eat. If it takes an hour to feed a healthy infant, then it is taking too long. Ask your Pediatrician.
- o Begin with 2 ounces at a time. Add more until the 30-minute mark. EXAMPLE: If the babies finish 3 ounces for two feedings in a row, then have 3 ½-4 ounces in the bottle for subsequent feedings. They do not have to finish it all, just have more to offer.

Position: Make sure that both you and your infant are comfortable.
- o Support your arm with a pillow or use the crook of your arm.
- o Hold the baby in a semi-upright position.
- o Tilt the bottle so that the nipple and the neck of the bottle are always filled with formula.

Changing formulas:
- o Do not change formulas without checking with your doctor.
- o If formula is changed:
  - o It will take the infant several days to adjust to a new formula
  - o Stools will change and may increase or decrease and can vary from firm to loose.
  - o Increased gassiness/fussiness

Temperature for feedings: You may try different temperatures from cool to warm to find which your infant prefers. If warming, place bottle in a cup of warm water and ALWAYS CHECK TEMPERATURE BEFORE FEEDING.

Note: Always follow the directions on the can. NEVER USE A MICROWAVE TO WARM BOTTLES. Microwaves heat unevenly and what you test on your wrist may feel fine, but portions of formula in the bottle can be scorching!

Note: Never reuse leftover formula from a bottle. The bottle must be finished or the un-used portion discarded after one hour. Once the baby's mouth has touched the bottle, bacteria has been introduced into the entire bottle. Refrigeration does not kill this bacteria.

Gas in formula fed infants: Some babies are just gassy.
- o May try different bottle systems.
- o May try different nipple sizes.
- o Burp well, try different positions when burping.
- o May use infant gas drops according to package directions.

VOMITING/
SPITTING UP

> **CALL** "My 3 month old is spitting up three and four times a day. She is gaining weight, and there is urine in every diaper. She is happy and hardly ever cries. It just ruins all her outifits."

Occasionally, spitting up bothers us as mothers more than it does the baby. Try to take your cues from how well the infant tolerates the spitting up.

There is a condition called GI reflux that can be treated with medication. If your baby is very fussy throughout the day and during feedings, contact your Pediatrician.

Vomiting/Spitting Up: occasionally babies will vomit and/or spit up after a feeding. When to be concerned:

- o Vomiting is persistent i.e. every 20-45 minutes regardless of feedings.
- o Vomiting large amounts at least 2-3 times a day for more than 2 days.
- o Forceful vomiting more than 6x/day.
- o Progressively getting worse with each feeding.
- o You can see the baby's stomach clenching within minutes after feeding begins.

- Unable to keep infant latched on.
- Fussy with feedings, during and after (although this alone can also indicate a growth spurt).
- Decreased wet diapers. We like to see at least 5 wet diapers in 24 hours. Check diaper well. You may want to place toilet tissue in the diaper to check for wetness because the absorbent nature of today's diapers makes it hard to tell if the baby has urinated at all.
- Inside of bottom lips is dry and tacky when you swipe it with your pinky finger.
- Abdomen hard and tender at rest. (Hard like a table top as opposed to soft like a real full balloon.)
- Blood in stool (more than 1 tsp bright red blood)
- **Seek immediate medical attention for a baby under 3 months old with a rectal temperature 100.4 F or higher**
- Call Pediatrician if the baby is older than three months and has a temp over 101.5 rectally.

Spitting up: measures to decrease amount and frequency. Some babies just spit up more than others. It is more related to physics than behavior. Spitting up usually resolves by 7 months although babies may have a resurgence of spitting up when they learn to sit up because there is more pressure on the abdomen as those muscles are developed.
- Reduce feeding by a ½ ounce. (In bottle fed babies who are over one month old with good weight gain.)

- Burp infant 2-3 times a feeding. Do this when the baby pauses in a feed. If there is not a pause, then try every 5-10 minutes.
- Place infant in a 35-45 degree angle (sitting position) for 20-30 minutes after the feeding. A bouncy seat is great for this.
- In healthy infants, nurse or feed no less than every 3 hours during the day.

Note: If the baby continues to spit up with every feeding, contact your Pediatrician.

GETTING YOUR BABY
TO SLEEP

Now here is the real reason most of you will be reading and loving this material! If you follow these directions (watching the DVD section entitled "Bath time and Bedtime Routine" will be enormously helpful) you will have a much better chance of enjoying your evenings and nights on into toddlerhood.

CALL "My baby is 2 months old, she cries every night and wakes up 3 or 4 times to feed. I am so exhausted I can hardly think straight."

After evaluating that there are no abnormal physical findings in this baby, the following advice—IF FOLLOWED—will produce a much better night's sleep.

Note: In a healthy baby more than 2 months old, who is gaining weight, there is no reason to have to wake up in the middle of the night several times to feed. They can learn to get what they need during the day.

Sleeping: Naptimes
- o In an area where there is light and moderate noise.
- o Put the baby in the crib while awake.
- o May use swaddle if needed.
- o May use white noise. We recommend

51

purchasing a sound soothing machine with no lights. They can be found at Target, Brookstone, and Sharper Image.
- o Naps should last no longer than 2 hour stretches at one time.

Sleeping: Bedtime Routines (older than 2 weeks)
- o Begins with bath time. (Wake infant up 15 minutes prior to bath, increasing this time as the baby gets older and can handle longer periods of alertness.)
- o After the bath, and once the baby is diapered and clothed, dim the lights, read a book, play soft music.
- o Feed very well. Burp.
- o Swaddle tightly (infants under 4 months old). Place in bed.
- o Turn on white noise
- o Make sure the room is dark. Avoid nightlights or closet lights. You may turn on minimal lighting when you go into the room to check on the baby so you do not trip.

Note: At **www.momsoncall.com** we offer a blanket in the perfect size and with just the right material for an effective swaddle because there were not any on the market that were suitable. This effective tight swaddle can make the difference between a baby that sleeps for one hour and one that sleeps 6-7 hours at night.

Middle of the night feedings - After the first two weeks and only if baby has proper weight gain (prior to two weeks old, feed on demand).

- o Always wait until they are truly crying; not fussing and just making noises, but crying.
- o Try to wait 5 minutes in the beginning, to make sure they do not go back to sleep.
- o Feed with the least amount of light that is safe and as little talking as possible.
- o Keep it boring. This feeding is strictly business.

If you would like your baby to sleep for 5-9 hours per night, follow these instructions to the letter. And remember to follow these steps for at least three nights in a row before you decide for certain if this is working for your infant.

Getting your baby to sleep is really this easy. They just need a solid routine and a tight swaddle. The sound soothing machines that are available at Target or Brookstone (for adults - so they do not have all those annoying lights) are an essential piece of the puzzle.

We have found that using a baby monitor that is unplugged from the base, so the static is loud enough for you to hear through the door, works just as well.

Use this routine and do not leave out one step! This has worked for hundreds of frustrated families and it is our hope that it will be just as effective for you and yours.

> **Note:** Once they are rolling over and scooting around in the bed, take blankets out of the bed.

CRYING

Healthy babies may cry on and off for 3-4 hours/day, more often in the evenings.

- o If the baby cries for 2 hours NON-STOP, your child needs to be seen. (That means that the baby does not have 5-10 minute periods of not crying.)
- o Occasionally check fingers, toes and penis (if applicable) for hair or thread wrapped around these areas. You need to look closely. If unable to remove hair, call your Pediatrician.
- o Also check eyes for redness or excessive watering when not crying. Occasionally a baby may scratch an eye with their fingernail.

Other common causes of crying in infants

Milk Allergies
- o Severe crying, usually after every feeding.
- o Vomiting.
- o Watery stools or stools with less than 1 teaspoon right red blood for more than 3 stools. (Do not have to be consecutive.)

Acid Reflux
- o Spitting up after every feeding, often painful high-pitched crying immediately thereafter.

- Forceful vomiting more than 3 times per day for more than 2 days.
- Crying with meals, day and night.
- Arching back. Unable to keep latched on breast/bottle.

Note: Always see your Pediatrician to check for any medical problems with continuous crying and/or vomiting.

Comfort Measures for the Crying Infant

- Swaddle tightly-remember if the swaddle is not tight, the baby will not like it. Some babies will act like they do not like it until it is done. The advantage of using a tight swaddle is that it keeps babies from startling themselves. Babies have not yet figured out how to control their limbs, this is very irritating if one is trying to get to sleep! You may begin to stop swaddling around 3-4 months.
- Tilt babies towards their bellies either on your forearm or across your lap, careful not to drop them.
- Turn on white noise. Needs to be louder than the crying.
- Constant motion, always supporting the head and neck.
- After your baby has calmed down, may try to give a pacifier. (Teach them to suck a pacifier by pulling on the pacifier while they are sucking and allowing them to pull it back in with the suction of their mouth.)

THE THREE-DAY RULE

> **CALL** "We are at my mom's for vacation and the baby does not want to sleep. She usually goes to sleep so well. She has just been fussy ever since we got here."

Might we mention that this baby will also probably take three days to adjust back to her sleep schedule once they return from vacation. This happens in our lives very often.

(Jennifer: I can remember going to my mother's house in North Carolina for the first time with the twins. It was chaos. The babies were off their normal routine and crying beyond belief. We stayed for a week. Three days into the trip, they calmed down and adjusted to their new surroundings. Then, when we came home, the same thing happened. They cried and screamed and would not go to bed for three more nights. It was exhausting, and I know what you are going through when you take trips or change routines.)

Take heart, the three day rule will ring true. Hang in there and keep that bedtime routine as consistent as possible. Knowing what to expect and living in that reality will greatly improve your ability to cope.

We have found that babies and toddlers require a three-day transition period in many areas. Do not get discouraged. Continue to provide a routine environment. Your child's sleep pattern may be interrupted when:

- o They reach certain developmental milestones - i.e. crawling, walking, speaking.
- o They change environments or daily routines (vacation, holidays).
- o They are recovering from an illness.

This is where the sleep cycle can meet its doom. It is hard to retrain your baby or toddler to go to sleep on their own and stay in bed for three days after all these interruptions. If you will stay committed, they will learn in generally three days. That is how long it takes a baby to establish a new routine or re-establish an old one. So, this means they will fuss and cry like they did when we were training them to go to sleep the first time at night. It gets better with each subsequent night.

When Laura moved her 2 year old into his new room, he did not want to take a nap. She put him in the childproof room and closed the door and allowed him to cry. The first day took about 20 minutes of crying, the second about 10 minutes, and by the third naptime he fussed about 2-3 minutes and was off to sleep. Did this break Laura's heart? Yes. Was this the best thing for Brent so he could learn to sooth himself to sleep? Yes.

FRUSTRATION

> **CALL** "I just can't let my baby be on his stomach at play time. He doesn't like it."

Children learn by practicing. They do the same thing over and over again. It may take 20-30 times of doing something the right way and/or the wrong way before they consistently do it the right way. Continue to allow them the opportunity to learn.

If your child is about to crawl and is crying for a toy across the room, do not get it for him. Their frustration level can motivate them to achieve developmental milestones.

Allow the baby a moderate level of frustration and crying after 3 months. Monitor and encourage them as they try to roll over, hold their chest up, and soothe themselves to sleep. (See DVD section on Frustration)

Babies cry. It is okay to allow your baby to cry 15-20 minutes at a time. They may cry on and off for 3-4 hours especially in the evening (usually when they get to 3-6 weeks old). We do not want your baby to have more than 2 hours of inconsolable crying and we are not asking you to ignore their basic needs such as diaper changes and feedings. Just be prepared for babies to cry for no apparent reason in the evenings and 15-20 minute segments during the day. It does not mean that you are doing something wrong.

TYPICAL DAYS

CALL "I just want to know what kind of schedule my baby should be on. I feel so lost."

Most babies thrive on a routine. However, **times are here as a guideline and can be adjusted to your schedule**. Remember, try to keep as close to you and your baby's daily routine as possible.

We understand that schedules these days need to be flexible. We just know that the babies who have regular nap times and feeding times tend to be more content. **There is a delicate balance between being so scheduled that you cannot enjoy life and being so flexible that you cannot enjoy your baby.**

Typical Day for 2 days to 4 weeks old : The baby/babies can be very fussy on the first night home from the hospital. Most of the time, babies are sleepy during the day and fussy at night. Babies can be difficult to awaken for feedings during the day. At night they may seem as if they want to feed every hour. They will adjust their schedules in a week or two. It is important that you try to sleep when the baby sleeps and recognize that this stage does not last forever. From one to four weeks, schedules are being established and they may vary considerably from day to day. Some babies are on a schedule from the start and just eat every 3 hours, day or night. You will know what kind of baby you have.

Typical Day: 4-8 week old:
- o 6 a.m. - Feed
- o 7 a.m.- Sleep
- o 9 a.m. - Feed. The baby is generally alert and playful and has mild, if any, fussiness.
- o 10 a.m.- Sleep
- o 12 noon - Feed. The baby is generally alert and playful, mild if any fussiness.
- o 1 p.m. Sleep
- o 3 p.m. Feed. The baby is generally alert and fussier than in the a.m.
- o 4 p.m. Sleep
- o 6 p.m. "Supper Feed" The baby is generally alert and playful, but will have increased fussiness as the night progresses.
- o 7 p.m. May sleep, may be increasingly fussy.
- o 8-9 p.m. Begin bath time routine (Stretch this time out so they are hungry for the "last feed" of the night.)
- o 9:30 Begin "Bedtime" Feeding
- o 10 p.m. Swaddle very well, put in bed, turn on white noise, and make sure the room is dark. Allow the babies to cry. (May let the baby cry for 2-5 minutes if under 3 months old. Try increasing that time as they get older.)
- o 2 a.m. If wakes (truly awakens—do not count whining, grunting, or straining), wait just a few minutes prior to feeding. Try pacifier.
- o 2:15 a.m. Feed (keep it boring).

61

o   5-6 a.m. Begin again.

    Allow them to sleep as late as they want to within reason. Adjust as needed for your schedule. Usually babies should start their day by 8-9 a.m.
    Another scenario is to feed "supper" closer to 7 p.m. start bath time at 9:30-10 p.m. and feed the "Bedtime" feeding around 10-10:30 or so. This is great to begin with for a couple of weeks.
    The most important thing is to always keep a minimum of 3 hours between "supper" feeding and "bedtime" feeding. The bedtime feeding should always come **after** the bath.

Typical Day 8-14 week old:
o   7 a.m.- Feed/Sleep or awake and playful
o   8:30 a.m.- Nap (ideally for 1-1 ½ hours)
o   10-10:30 a.m.- Feed
o   12 noon-Nap
o   2 p.m.-Feed. The baby is generally alert and playful with mild fussiness.
o   3 p.m.- Nap
o   4:30-5:30p.m.- "Supper Feed" The baby is generally alert and playful with fussiness increased from the a.m.
o   6 p.m.- Catnap
o   7 p.m.- Wake-up, stimulate, play - this time on and off fussiness may be moderate-severe.
o   7:30 p.m.- Begin bath time routine
o   8 p.m.- Bedtime feeding/routine

When sleeping from 10 p.m. to 6 a.m. consistently, you may begin to start the bath time/bedtime routine earlier.

When starting the bath time/bedtime routine earlier, some feedings combine. So one feeding may need to be 2 ½ hours apart and the next closer to four hours. Remember to keep in mind the "Supper" and "Bedtime" feedings are the only ones that need to be a minimum of 3 hours apart.

Occasionally, during a growth spurt, babies may go through "Cluster Feedings." This means that they want to feed every hour for 3-4 hours. This may occasionally mess up your schedule. It is okay and will pass in 2-3 days.

The amount of milk your body produces generally depletes as the day goes on. That often makes breastfed babies a little fussier with evening feedings. It is fine to supplement at those feedings.

You will begin to take the baby out of the swaddle around 3-4 months of age. (Earlier if the baby is wiggling out on his/her own.)

Remember, for every change that occurs in the baby's routine, allow them 3 days to adjust. 3 DAYS, 3 DAYS, 3 DAYS.

SECTION THREE: SAFETY ISSUES

WAYS TO KEEP YOUR BABY SAFE

"I will lift my eyes to the hills- from whence comes my help? My help comes from the Lord, who made heaven and earth. He will not allow your foot to be moved; He who keeps you will not slumber. Behold, He who keeps Israel shall neither slumber or sleep.
The Lord is your keeper; The Lord is your shade at your right hand. The sun shall not strike you by day, nor the moon by night."

Psalm 121:1-6

IMMUNIZATIONS

CALL "Can I give my baby Tylenol before his immunizations to help it not to hurt so bad?"

Tylenol will not take away the pain of the actual injection, however, the baby will have forgotten the incident by the time you walk out the door. (It will probably take you much longer to forget.) We all get through it. We hate it, but we do get through it.

Site
- o Given in thighs.
- o May be red and/or swollen for 2-3 days at site of injections.
- o May have small pea-sized knots for several weeks after discoloration resolves.

Fever
- o Fever 101 up to 103.5 rectally is expected.
- o Tylenol may be given every 4 hours. See package instructions.

When to seek medical care
- o Temp over 103.5 rectally
- o Crying inconsolably for 2 hours
- o Seizure activity (uncontrollable shaking)
- o Signs of allergic reaction (very rare) generally will happen within the first 15-20 min after administration of immunizations.

- Difficulty Breathing
- Wheezing
- Hives
- Pale and clammy
- Difficulty Swallowing

Moms on Call LLC is in favor of vaccinating children. It is what the American Academy of Pediatrics recommends. Although the MMR (Measles Mumps and Rubella) vaccine is not administered until one year of age, you may have heard about studies linking MMR vaccine with Autism. There are studies that disprove this theory. However, that is the nature of studies. It takes several years and millions of dollars to make any definite connections. This much we **do** know. That prior to the MMR vaccination over 100,000 children a year died of these combined diseases. If your child does not get immunized and contracts one of these diseases, it puts them and other children at risk, especially the children under one year who have not yet been vaccinated.

The types of vaccinations that your child will get at 2, 4 and 6 months generally include:
- DTP (Tetanus Diptheria Pertussis)
- IPV (Injectable Polio Vaccine)
- Prevnar (Protects against a bacteria that can cause meningitis and pneumonia)
- HIB (Haemophilus B Influenzae - another bacteria that can cause meningitis)
- Hep B (Hepatitis B - a disease of the liver transmitted through the blood and body fluids of infected carriers)

Some of these immunizations are combined in one shot, so the most your child should get at one time is four shots; two in one thigh, two in the other. It is over very quickly.

After immunizations the baby is generally a little sleepier for 3-4 hours then possibly fussy for the next 4-6. You can take the band-aids off after about an hour. If the baby is fussy or develops a fever, use Tylenol every four hours as needed.

Note: In the summertime, especially when baby's legs are exposed, they may try to pull off the band-aid and eat it. Watch carefully!

CHILDPROOFING/SAFETY

> **Real situation:** *A 3 year old chokes on a carrot at home and mom does not know what to do. Luckily, the urgent care was minutes from her house. She drove him to the urgent care and the nurses there dislodged the carrot before he became unresponsive. Close call yes! Did this mom want to take CPR classes after that? YES!*

Childproofing: Accidents are just that— ACCIDENTS. However, there are measures that we can take to minimize our child's risk. According to the American Heart Association, injuries are the leading cause of death in children and young adults. Childproofing and being knowledgeable about possible hazards can help you minimize that risk for your child.

We find that parents spend much more time worrying about the relatively low risk of possible meningitis and less time worrying about the most common risk - injuries.

We cannot stress enough the importance of taking regular CPR training. The question you should ask yourself and your child's caretakers is not only, "When did you take your last CPR class?" but more importantly, "if my child were choking or unresponsive, would I know what to do?" (Yes, I know you said "Call 911" in your head but there are life saving steps that you can take while 911 is on the way!)

Please, Please, Please, know what to do if

your child is choking. CPR classes are offered through the American Heart Association and the Red Cross. Almost all area hospitals offer regular classes. Jennifer is an instructor and offers classes in the Atlanta area.

Common Safety Issues. Here is a Quick but not exhaustive checklist for some common safety issues.

- o Put plastic guards on all sharp corners.
- o Outlet protectors for outlets not being used and an outlet cover attachment that can be used on outlets that *are* being used. Children will try to play with cords that are plugged in.
- o Keep blind cords short and out of reach of children.
- o Put safety latches on all cabinets and drawers.
- o Move all cleaning supplies from under the sink and put in a high cabinet that locks.
- o Put plastic doorknob covers on doors and a hook-eye latch on any doors leading to basements or stairs.
- o Keep a set of keys to all doors in case your child locks themselves in a room.
- o Keep all plastic bags out of reach - including dry cleaner bags and grocery bags.
- o Infant gates to top and bottom of stairs. Do not use pressure-mounted gates, use hardware mounted.
- o Never allow your child to play with latex balloons. They generally like to bite them and they can inhale a piece of latex and

choke or suffocate. No balloons in the car.

o Check the safety of the crib. Slats should be no wider than 2 3/8 inches apart. There should be no more than 2 inches between the mattress edges and the crib.

o Do not put any pillows, stuffed animals or anything for that matter in the bed. If you think your child needs warmth then use a sleeper.

Bathroom

o Keep all medicines in a locked cabinet and out of baby's reach. This means no bottles of vitamins or Advil on the counter, even with "childproof" caps.

o Keep shampoo and soap out of reach.

o Always unplug any appliances to avoid electric shock.

o Set hot water heater to 120 degrees F. Always check temperature of water before placing child in it.

o Be aware of what you put in the trash, i.e. pills or razor blades. These items should be put in a trashcan out of child's reach.

o Put toilet locks on all toilets. I know dad does not like this but children are fascinated with the toilet and can fall in. They also like to flush items down the toilet and dad will not like having to pull the items from the toilet or taking apart the toilet to extract the large clump of play-doh. (Thanks, Patrick and Blake— Laura.)

- o Always empty water out of the bathtub.
- o Put non-skid bath mats on bottom of tub.
- o NEVER LEAVE YOUR CHILD UNATTENDED IN THE BATH FOR ANY REASON-which means, if the phone rings, let it ring! They can leave a message.

Kitchen
- o Always turn pot and pan handles to the back of the stove and cook on back burners.
- o Avoid tablecloths. They can be pulled down with hot food sliding onto baby's head. (Once Laura's son pulled a tablecloth and a pot of hot grits fell on Laura's foot. The burn marks are still there.)
- o Keep all appliances out of reach.
- o Place covers on stove controls and a lock on the refrigerator. (They sell these in all colors so they match your kitchen décor.)
- o Always be aware of where your child is when transporting hot foods or liquids.
- o HOUSE RULE: NO toys on the kitchen floor. You can trip and drop hot liquid on kids.
- o Keep aluminum foil and saran wrap out of reach.
- o Make sure the stove is anchored to the wall. Make sure all knives and cutlery are out of reach. Sometimes latches on a drawer are not quite enough.
- o Never keep kid snack food near any medications, vitamins, or cleaners. (They learn where the snack food is and that is

the cabinet they try to get into when you are not looking.)

Living Area
- o Be aware of windows. These should have safety locks so they can only be opened a few inches. (May be purchased at home improvement stores.)
- o Check all furniture to see if it falls over easily, bookcases especially. Where *we* see a bookcase, a little boy sees a ladder. Anchor your bookcases to the wall. (Trust me, Bryce loved to try this— Jennifer).
- o Keep electrical cords out of reach. TV cord can be pulled and cause the TV to come crashing down on a child's head.
- o Never leave your child alone with pets.
- o Always check stair railing for sturdiness.

Choking. Liquid that is swallowed at meals will usually clear itself in 10-30 seconds.
Solids:
- o If the child is coughing vigorously and can talk and breathe, then do nothing. Do not slap a child on the back who may be choking when they are in the upright position. This can lodge the foreign object in the throat.
- o Removal of a foreign object is best learned in a CPR class.
- o Do not put your fingers in the child's mouth unless you see an object, then and only then can you perform a finger sweep of the mouth.

Car Seats

o It is best to have your car seat checked by a professional. www.Nhtsa.dot.org will list area checkpoints. Some local fire departments will also check.

o Your car seat will come with weight limits. Check the side and back for information on placement and weight requirements.

o Infants should be rear-facing and in the second row of vehicle seats until one year AND 20 pounds.

o Straps need to be snug. The front clip should be at the nipple line and no more than two of your fingers should fit between the strap and your child. Again, note the manufacturer's guidelines. If you have any questions, see a checkpoint near you.

o When tightening the seat in the car, put your knee in the base of the car seat. Then thread seatbelt through the car seat according to manufacturer's guidelines. The seat should move no more than ½ inch from side to side. Always remember to use the additional safety clip (often sold separately) to clip to the seatbelt. The safest place to put a car seat is in the middle of the back seat. Never put a child under 12 years old in the front seat of a car with an airbag. The airbag can deploy with such force that it instantly kills a child. Never put the car seat in the front seat of a car with airbags.

o Many newer model cars come with a tether attachment in the rear of the vehicle. Tether equipment can also be purchased at most baby stores.

QUICK-GRAB FIRST AID KIT

> CALL "We are out of town and I think my baby has a fever but we forgot to bring a thermometer."

You will need the following items when you least expect it. Keep one in the car and one at home. These are to be kept out of the reach of children. We recommend buying a container with a handle and a lid. On the inside of the lid, list the Pediatrician's number and the number of Poison Control.

- Band-Aids
- Tylenol
- Benadryl
- A "B-D" digital thermometer
- Cortaid
- Polysporin
- Anti-bacterial wash
- Hydrogen Peroxide or Betadine
- Pack of 4x4 Gauze and 2x2 Gauze
- Ace Bandage
- Squeezable ice pack
- Tweezers
- Dressing tape

POISONING

POISON CONTROL
404-616-9000 (Atlanta area)
1-800-222-1222 (other areas)

Always call your poison control center immediately if you think your child has swallowed a poison.

You will be asked the following:
o What was swallowed?
o How much? Always estimate the maximum amount.
o How long ago it was swallowed?
o What symptoms, if any is the child showing now?
o Age and approximate weight of child.

Prevention
o Keep all chemicals, medicines, and cleaners out of reach and locked!
o Get a list from Pike's Nursery (or your local plant supplier) of any poisonous house or outdoor plants. Holly berries are poisonous. Get rid of all poisonous house plants.
o Keep alcoholic beverages out of reach and locked.

SECTION FOUR: THE LABYRINTH OF HEALTH CARE

HOW TO NAVIGATE THROUGH THE HEALTH CARE SYSTEM

"Come, let Us go down there and confuse their language, that they may not understand one another's speech" Genesis 11:7

YOUR DOCTOR'S OFFICE

People at your doctor's office

Front desk personnel-They cannot answer medical questions. They handle day-to-day operations such as locating your chart, making copies of records, and making appointments.

Billing and insurance- These folks are trained in billing. They do not answer medical questions. They may also be in charge of doing electronic referrals to specialists, which contacts your insurance to let them know why your child requires a specialist's care.

Office manager – This person is in charge of running the office. Generally, they are in charge of personnel. They would handle complaints about office policies or poor customer service.

Staff Nurse- These nurses generally call you into the back office area and grill you with questions; which the doctor will soon ask you again. However, there are many levels of nurses. (Not all are trained to answer your medical questions.) There is a trend in office care to hire the least expensive back office help available, which is a medical assistant. Here is our understanding of the educational background of the people who may be asking you questions, taking blood specimens, and giving immunizations.

- Medical Assistant-High School diploma and graduated from a medical program that lasted 6-12 months. Trained in basic medical procedures such as vital signs and drawing blood.
- LPN- (Licensed practical nurse) High School Diploma. Went through a 1-2 year program and took a national licensing exam. Trained in dispensing medication and basic medical procedures. Also trained in basic disease processes and administering medications and immunizations.
- RN- (Registered Nurse) High School Diploma. Have at least a 2-year college degree plus took a 2-year nursing program. Took a national licensing exam. Trained in all above plus in-depth disease process, decision making, and patient monitoring.
- BSN - (Bachelor's Degree in Nursing) - Graduated from an accredited college of nursing that offered a 4-year program. Trained in all above plus administrative and ethical decision making.
- Lab Tech. - High School Diploma and 6-12 month program. Trained in obtaining specimens of all sorts (including urine, blood and feces), how to order tests, decipher insurance information, and how to run a laboratory.

We have worked with people from all these specialties. There are some Medical Assistants who are wonderful and some who are not. Some RNs who have worked with us are wonderful and some are not. It is always best to ask your questions in the office to the doctor during the visit. Some advice is different because of the nature of the information. *i.e.* not all doctors prefer the same brand of formula. When calling your doctor's office for advice, the office should have trained phone triage personnel who can answer your questions. The doctors will seldom answer your questions over the phone themselves. In the offices where we have worked, we have over 125 calls a day and if the doctors had to answer them, there would be no time to see sick children. There are instances when the doctor likes to handle questions over the phone personally and it would be a good idea to speak with your doctor about what instances those are.

Our understanding of those who can diagnose and treat your child at the office

Doctor - graduated from an accredited college of Medicine and took a national licensing exam.

Nurse Practitioner - An RN who went back to school to a 2-4 year program that concentrated on diagnosis and treatment of disease processes. These practitioners are usually very patient-oriented and if your child's case goes beyond their comfort level or educational expertise, they will call in the doctor to give a second opinion.

Physician's Assistant - Not necessarily a nurse, but admission to the P.A. school requires a general knowledge of medical practices. They must also have a minimum of a high school diploma before being considered for the P.A. program. This is a 2-year program that also concentrates on diagnosis and treatment of disease processes. P.A.s are generally more procedure oriented and are trained to assist with minor surgical procedures.

SCHEDULING APPOINTMENTS

If you ever had to wait for your appointment with a screaming child after a night of absolutely no sleep, you have probably been frustrated by this difficult system.

o Main schedule - This is a master schedule that has been set in place by the doctors in advance. It dictates when and how many appointments will be available each day. For example, there can be six Physical Exam slots- three in the a.m. and three in the afternoon. Sick visits may be every 15 minutes in between.

o Working Schedule - Changes that are made to the Main Schedule to accommodate every day challenges. For example, it is the middle of flu season and more sick visits need to be added to accommodate all the sick patients.

The Long Wait: It is virtually impossible, even if you grill each parent before an appointment is made, to schedule the exact time each visit will take. "My child just has an ear infection. It will only take a second." can turn into newly diagnosed Reactive Airway Disease that requires 2 breathing treatments, complicated take home medicines and a thorough explanation. We have seen this happen many times.

Here are some tips to help your doctor's office stay on time.

- Be clear about what you want to be addressed at the visit.
- If you think you may want other siblings seen, say so when you are scheduling the appointment. Try not to ask the doctor, once you are in the room, if they can see the sibling. If it turns out that you do not want the other child seen, it is much easier to cancel that appointment than it is to stop everything, find the chart, make the right paperwork, and fit another child in front of existing appointments. If you have ever had to wait at the office, this is a big reason why. On occasion, you simply do not realize that the other child is sick until after you are put in the back office. Just try to evaluate both children prior to your visit if you can.
- **Arrive on time** - We know, why do you have to be on time, when we often take 20-30 minutes to get you to the back office? Well, it is essential that we have a good idea of which patients are coming and at what time. Occasionally we have to "fit in" a child who is urgently very sick. Some appointments are scheduled at times directly before lunch or closing time. It can require five or six employees in order to facilitate your visit from check-in to check-out. In the winter season doctors and nurses rarely get more than a 20 minute break, please be understanding.

One Saturday the office that we work with was open from 8:30-11 a.m. At

11:30, as the staff was getting ready to leave, a mom walks through the door with her son, in his soccer uniform and demands to be seen. "What is the problem today" The front desk asked. "I think he has strep" the mother replied. As it turns out, the mom had knowingly taken this child to a soccer game when he had a fever and sore throat, exposing both teams to what turned out to be strep throat.

This is not a mistake anyone wants to repeat and this mom was really not looking forward to making that dreaded call to the coach.

If you think your child is sick and definitely if they have fever, make an appointment and come to the office. Our kids play sports and we understand the disappointment they feel when they are unable to participate. However, I am sure the other moms at the game would appreciate our consideration.

- o **Have your insurance card ready**. Yes, the insurance agencies require that we prove that you showed proof of insurance for every visit. They can deny a claim and postpone or deny payment to your Pediatrician's office if the office cannot provide proof that you showed current insurance coverage. "Nothing has changed" is unfortunately a thing of the past.
- o **Be Understanding** - There are times when children become critically ill very quickly and we have to address the most

life threatening situations first. On some days this could mean that we have to "work-in" 5 or 6 very sick children. There is no way to plan for how many or how severe the complaints can be. One critically ill child can throw off a schedule by an hour or more. The thing to remember is that your child would receive the same treatment. If your child is in imminent danger, we would make others wait to care for your child.

o **If you think that you have been overlooked, alert the front office staff politely and they can check into the wait.** Different doctors have different schedules, Doctor A may be running on time and Doctor B an hour behind. Sometimes the staff may ask if you want to see another practitioner. Sometimes there is nothing that can be done. Asking politely can alert the front office if the charts got out of order or got misplaced.

PHONE TRIAGE

Here is our specialty! - With a large call volume, especially in the winter, it can take up to an hour or more to get a question answered. Here are some tips to help you make this a positive experience.

- o If you are calling about a general question such as feeding issues, it is best to wait until the slower periods, between 11a.m.-12p.m. or after 2 p.m. on Tues-Friday. **Monday morning is the worst time to call with a general question.** If you can avoid Monday all together, that would be even better.

- o **Ask questions during the visit. Make a list before your visit,** so you do not forget in the hustle and bustle of what is going on at the visit. If you have a physical scheduled, do not call 2 days in advance to ask general questions. The check-up is designed to address those concerns.

- o **Ask general questions during office hours.** After-hours phone triage is designed to determine if your child needs to go to the Emergency Room or not. It is not the time to discuss bowel habits in detail. If you have medication questions or are wondering if your child needs immediate medical attention, call after hours. Diaper rash is not an after hour emergency. We would rather have you call than to be worried about your child on any account, but please be courteous and do not abuse this privilege because it just fits in your schedule better. In the winter months especially, we are inundated with calls about very sick children. So call if you need to call, but take time to consider if your call could be managed during office hours.

- o **If you do not hear back from the office in one hour, call back.** If it is winter and the call volume is overwhelming then the front office will tell you. However, there are several reasons that we may be unable to reach you, such as numbers entered incorrectly, computer malfunction, or human error. We do not look at a call and say "Oh, that's silly, I'm not calling *her* back." After hours, if you call and need to speak to the phone nurse, you should receive a call back. The same goes for after hours calls. If you do not hear back in 30 minutes, call the number again and tell the answering service. Do this until you hear from your Pediatrician's office. If you have an issue that cannot wait 30 minutes then you should head to the local Emergency Room.
- o **Be available.** We know it is difficult to stay put for an hour and sometimes even impossible, but be clear as to what number you can be reached for the next hour. Do not call at a time when you know you will be at 2 or 3 different numbers.

- **Do not expect antibiotics to be dispensed over the phone.** It is unsafe medical practice to prescribe antibiotic therapy over the phone especially for a child who has not been examined. On several occasions that "ear infection" that mom was so sure of turned out to be meningitis or pneumonia. Taking antibiotics when your child does not need them can make the antibiotics ineffective when they do need them. I'd rather come to the office every time I think my child has an ear infection, than put his life at risk when he is hospitalized for pneumonia and his immune system does not respond to treatment. I promise that we do not ask you to come into the office just to irritate you or collect your $10 co-pay.
- **Read the information that the Pediatrician's office sends home with you after a visit.** We get many calls about immunization side effects. These are addressed on several fliers we send home after immunizations are given. **It is a good idea to have a file or drawer where you store these items and look through this information prior to calling.** If the answer you are looking for is unclear or not included in the flier, then call.

MEDICAL INSURANCE

In a nutshell, Medical insurance is a group of people who agree to pay a premium (set amount) every month. That money is invested and set aside to pay for medical treatments for the people in that specific group. It works because many people pay and then do not need expensive medical treatments. However, just because you have insurance, does not mean that all medical expenses are covered. Some insurance companies do not pay for mental health services, some do not cover physical or occupational therapy. Some do not cover certain drugs. If you are on an insurance plan, you probably have a textbook that outlines all of the treatments that are covered by your insurance policy. You may need a law degree to decipher what they all mean, but it is your responsibility to be aware of your insurance company rules and regulations.

Common problems:

o **Unsure of Co-Pay amount** - Co-Pay (amount you pay at time of service) should be listed on your card. If it is not, contact your insurance company and ask for a list of co-pays. Your co-pay for the doctor's office may be different then your co-pay for an emergency room visit.

o **Do not have a Primary Care Doctor**. Your insurance company lists all the doctors you can see in that insurance plan. Some even require that you choose one doctor to be your "Primary Care

Physician" (the one doctor you always have to see, who is the gatekeeper. He decides and refers you to other specialists and orders lab work.) If you have to choose a Primary Care Physician, generally all the doctors that practice in the same office are covered by your plan.

o **Unsure what laboratory or drugs are approved.** Some insurance companies only pay for certain drugs, or allow your child's testing to be done at certain laboratories. This list can change monthly. If your insurance has a website, print out a copy of current drugs that are approved and what laboratories are approved prior to your visit. This list will help your doctor and make for less time spent at the pharmacy.

o **Unsure if there is a need for a referral**. Again let us say that a referral does not mean that the insurance company will pay for services, it is only a notification process. It generally takes 2-3 business days to have a referral approved. You can check on the status of a referral by calling the customer service number on your card. It is a good idea to do this at least 2 days prior to a visit to a specialist or before having a procedure at the hospital.

o **Do not know what insurance "plan" you carry.** There is HMO, PPO or POS and many other kinds of insurance plans. Your specific **type** of plan is not always listed on the card. Contact your insurance company today and find out what "plan" you are on. You can write that information on the back of your card as long as you do not obstruct any printed information. This information is essential.

WHO'S WHO AT THE HOSPITAL

If your child needs to go to the hospital, you will encounter many men and women dressed in scrubs and hospital wear. Here's an idea of who they may be.

- o **Doctors** - They usually have their name embroidered on a white lab coat. Surgeons usually wear scrubs. They should introduce themselves upon entering your child's room. The doctor on call from your child's pediatric office will usually come to see your child the morning after admission. These doctors will usually come to your room between 6 a.m. and 9 a.m. or after 5 p.m. If you have questions for them at other times, you can ask your nurse.
- o **Staff Nurses** - Your nurse at the hospital has RN, BSN, or LPN on her badge. She administers your child's medication and assesses your child every shift. She is also the one to answer your questions and organize your child's procedures.
- o **Nursing Assistant** - Helps take care of basic needs, such as changing bed linens and taking vital signs. They are not trained in disease processes and do not answer medical questions.
- o **Physical Therapist** - Trained in how to use movement to aid in the healing process. They organize an exercise and movement regimen and help teach you

and your child how to move. These are prevalent in Orthopedic units.
- Respiratory Therapist - Trained in how to assess lung function and breathing. They can give breathing treatments and arrange for oxygen if it is needed.
- IV team - Some hospitals have a staff dedicated to starting and maintaining your child's I.V. They also do not know about your child's specific medical status.
- Lab Tech - Trained in how to draw blood and collect body fluids for testing. They also do not know about your child's specific medical condition.
- Educators - These staff help you to understand treatments and train you for home care. They are often Licensed Nurses.
- Food services - They deliver and pick up meals. It is easy to get meal plans wrong because they change frequently. Ask your nurse what your child's meal plan specifications are so you can know if your child has the right type of food, i.e., bland, low salt. If you know your child is diabetic, the little sheet of paper that comes on the food tray should say low-sugar or diabetic diet. Do not assume the Jell-O is sugar free.
- Housekeeping - Can come in at any time and change the trash bags or take care of spills.
- Maintenance - Can fix the air-conditioner or equipment in the room. If your air conditioner is not working properly, you may have to wait all day to

get Maintenance to arrive. Keep in mind that they are taking care of a large facility.

- **Nursing Supervisor** - You will probably never see this person. They manage staff complaints and arrange for appropriate staffing.
- **Billing** - You are usually required to stop by the billing office after discharge to discuss your bill. In some cases payment is required. Payment plans are usually an option if you are unable to pay the full amount. If you have insurance, the hospital will generally bill you after the insurance has paid their portion.
- **Patient Advocates** - If you are experiencing any problems, from arranging for childcare so you can stay with a sick sibling to financial concerns, the patient advocate can direct you to the right helper.
- **Chaplain** - There are often several faiths represented in the Chaplaincy of the local hospital. If you are Catholic and would like the elements, it can often be arranged through the Chaplain. If you need someone to listen or pray with you for your child's care, they are an amazing resource.
- **Lactation Consultants** - They are usually nurses with specialized training in the area of breastfeeding. They can often be accessed even after you leave the hospital by calling the hospital and asking for the "Lactation Department".

THE EMERGENCY ROOM/ URGENT CARE

Emergency services at a hospital include all of the people mentioned above, but the E.R. also acts like its own specialized area. It is important to note that the purpose of the ER or ED as some are now called (for Emergency Department), is to get your child out of immediate danger.

The ER is not a place to diagnose or treat long-term illness. They do not manage immunizations or basic child care. They are mainly there for life or death situations. Yes, they can diagnose the insidious ear infection or strep throat and prescribe antibiotics for such. However, their primary purpose is to evaluate your child and make sure that they are not in any immediate danger.

And if your child is in danger, they manage the situation until the child is in stable enough condition to either be sent home or be admitted to a room in the hospital. This is why the wait can be so long.

If your child is not in immediate danger, he/she may have to wait in order of urgency. (That means the car accident victim, possible meningitis and asthma attack get to go first.)

There are many childhood illnesses that are either life-threatening or nothing that even requires treatment. For example, we had a call about a nine-year old girl who was complaining of chest pain. She had strenuous activity over the past two days and also complained of indigestion. She had been awakened at night by this chest pain. She also had a fever and flu-like symptoms. Now, these are all early indicators of possible pericarditis (very possibly a life-threatening heart condition.) Pericarditis is not exceptionally common in this age group however, it is a possibility. These symptoms could also be heartburn or muscle strain. The difference is life and death. The only way to determine exactly what is happening, is to have a competent doctor examine the patient and order appropriate tests.

You may find yourself in the ER with a child who gets sent home for monitoring and you are wondering why you ever went through all that waiting and worrying. Pediatrics is not an exact science in most cases. It is better to be safe then sorry so the saying goes.

General Procedure @ the ER:
1) **Check-in** - This is where you give your information and show your insurance card and sign that you will pay for the services delivered. If your child is in immediate danger, when you enter the ER, yell for help. Life-threatening emergencies do not have to check-in before treatment.
2) **Waiting for Triage** - After you check-in, you are sent to the waiting area. You will be called from this area to be examined and questioned by a nurse. Vital signs are taken and the nurse evaluates how urgently your child needs to be seen. This evaluation is relative to how sick the other children in the ER appear.
3) **Waiting to go to an ER room.** After the

triage nurse evaluates your child, you are sent back to the waiting room. In the winter, this step could take several hours.

4) **Called to ER room** - A nurse will then put you in a room and ask more questions. Sometimes an IV is started or vital signs are taken again.

5) **The doctor comes** - A doctor questions you again and then decides what testing should be done. The tests are done in different parts of the hospital depending on what is ordered. Once an x-ray is ordered, it is put on the X-ray schedule and you wait for that department to come and get your child and do the x-ray. Lab work is the same. Then you wait for results. When the results come in, the doctor reviews them and either orders more tests or determines the problem and treats your child. Then you either go home or wait again for a room in the hospital to come available.

The ER manages emergency situations. Once you leave the ER, your child's care should be handled by their Primary Care Doctor. Sometimes children are released from the ER and then have another life-threatening episode. If this is the case then return to the ER. Your Pediatrician will generally not come to see your child in the Emergency Department; they leave that assessment up to the discretion of the Emergency Room Physicians. Some hospitals will have a staff of Admitting Doctors, who follow your care even after your child has been admitted. These physicians will come daily to your child's room and perform evaluations and order tests and medicines. They keep in touch with your Pediatrician by phone and fax. If you have this kind of doctor, your own Pediatrician will not come to see your child in the hospital. The Admitting Physicians are often Internal Medicine doctors and are quite skilled at the types of things that cause children to be hospitalized.

THE SPECIALIST'S OFFICE

Your doctor has a general knowledge of a variety of medical conditions. However, specific treatment for a disease process or condition may require a doctor who only specializes in that one area. If that is the case, your doctor will recommend that you make an appointment with a Specialist.

In Pediatrics, there are many specialties. It is best to have your primary care doctor determine which specialist is needed. Many specialist's offices have long waiting times before an appointment is available. If your child's situation is urgent, your child's primary care doctor can sometimes call and try to get your child in to see the specialist as soon as possible.

o Make sure the specialist is on your insurance. You can either call the customer service number on your card or look on the website for a listing.

o Call your doctor's office and tell the referral coordinator the name of the specialist, and the date and time of the appointment.

o Call your insurance company two days in advance of your appointment to check on the status of your referral. You can ask whether or not it has been approved.

o Have your insurance card ready the day of the appointment.

If you do not take these steps, often times

100

you will have to wait at the specialist's office. Their staff will require time to call the insurance company and your doctor's office. This process can take up to an hour. I am sure none of us wants to wait with our child for an hour in any office!

If you do not need a referral, then off to the specialist you go.

SOME INTERESTING CALLS FROM PARENTS YOU MIGHT ENJOY

"Yes, a chicken just fell on my child's head." *(Turned out to be a frozen chicken and very heavy. The child was unharmed.)*

"I have an emergency, I am at the store and I cannot find a puff-a-lump pet for my daughter." *Wow, should we come now or send the ambulance!*

2 A.M. "Yes, I am calling for my child's strep test result from last week." Reply, "How is your child doing now?" "Oh, she is sleeping and doing fine I just wanted to know if it ever turned out positive." "That can be handled during regular office hours."

"I think my baby is fine but my mom told me to dip my baby's pacifier in rum and then let her suck on it to calm her down." *We do not recommend that for the baby.*

7 P.M. A dad calls to report a child with a fever of 103. We asked, "Where did you put the thermometer?" Dad replies dryly "Back on the shelf." "No, I meant, where on the child?"

"What do you think this rash looks like" *Unfortunately we cannot see skin rashes over the phone.*

"I am calling about my son. His testicles are awfully small and I do not think that is normal. I certainly do not have that problem."

2:30 A.M. "Yes, I need to know what to do if my child is constipated." "How is the child now?" "Oh, she is fine, she is asleep in her room, I was just lying here thinking that I am not sure what to do if she ever got constipated." "So she has not been having any problems with her bowel movements." "No, not yet." "It is two-thirty in the morning. Ma'am, with all due respect, if she ever actually gets constipated, call us"

9:00 P.M. Pager read "Child hit in head with another head."

Additional Books Moms-On-Call recommends

o "Happiest Baby on the Block" - Karp
o "Your Baby's First Year" - American Academy of Pediatrics
o "Medications and Mother's Milk"- Hale